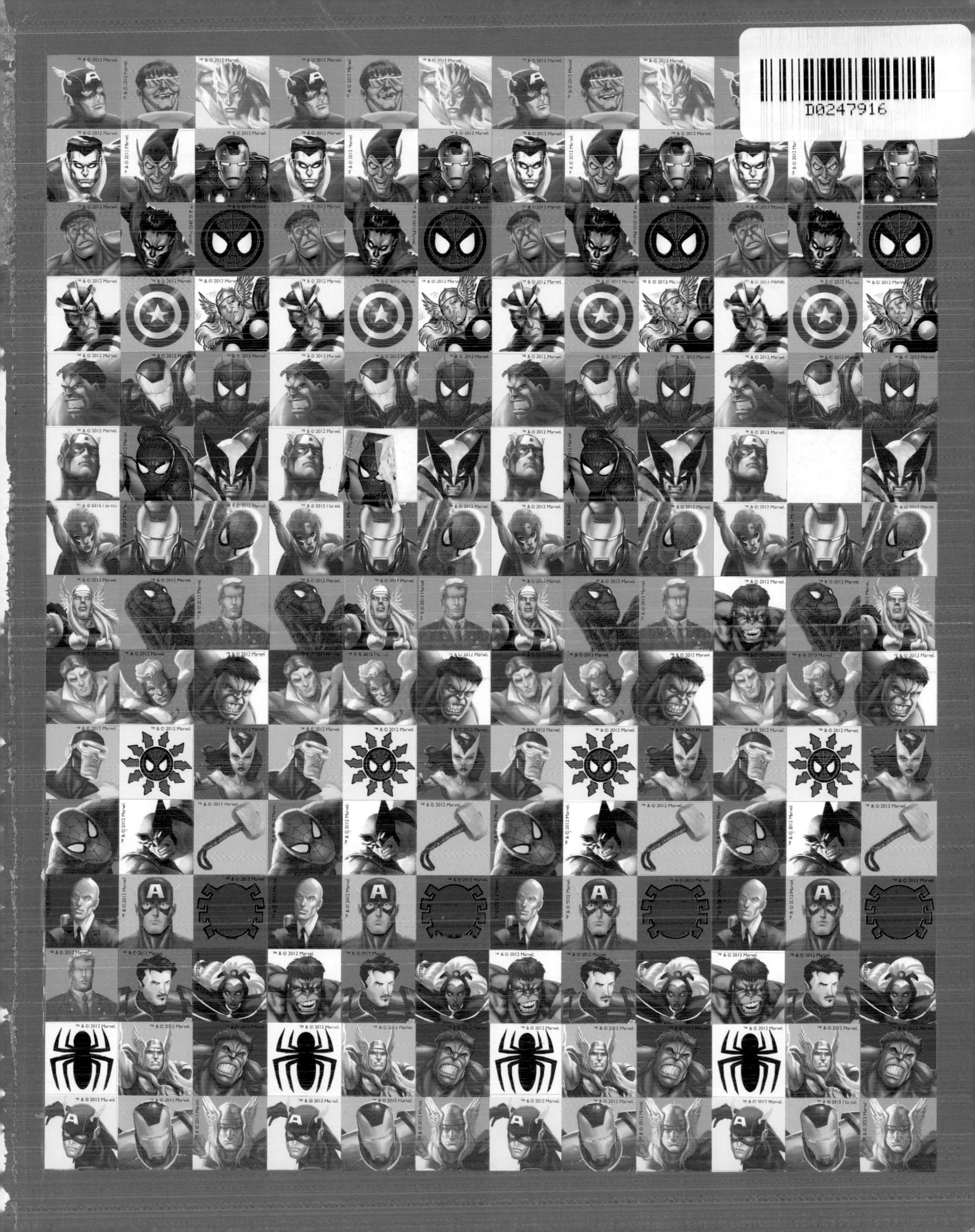
TM & © 2012 Marvel.

TM & © 2012 Marvel.

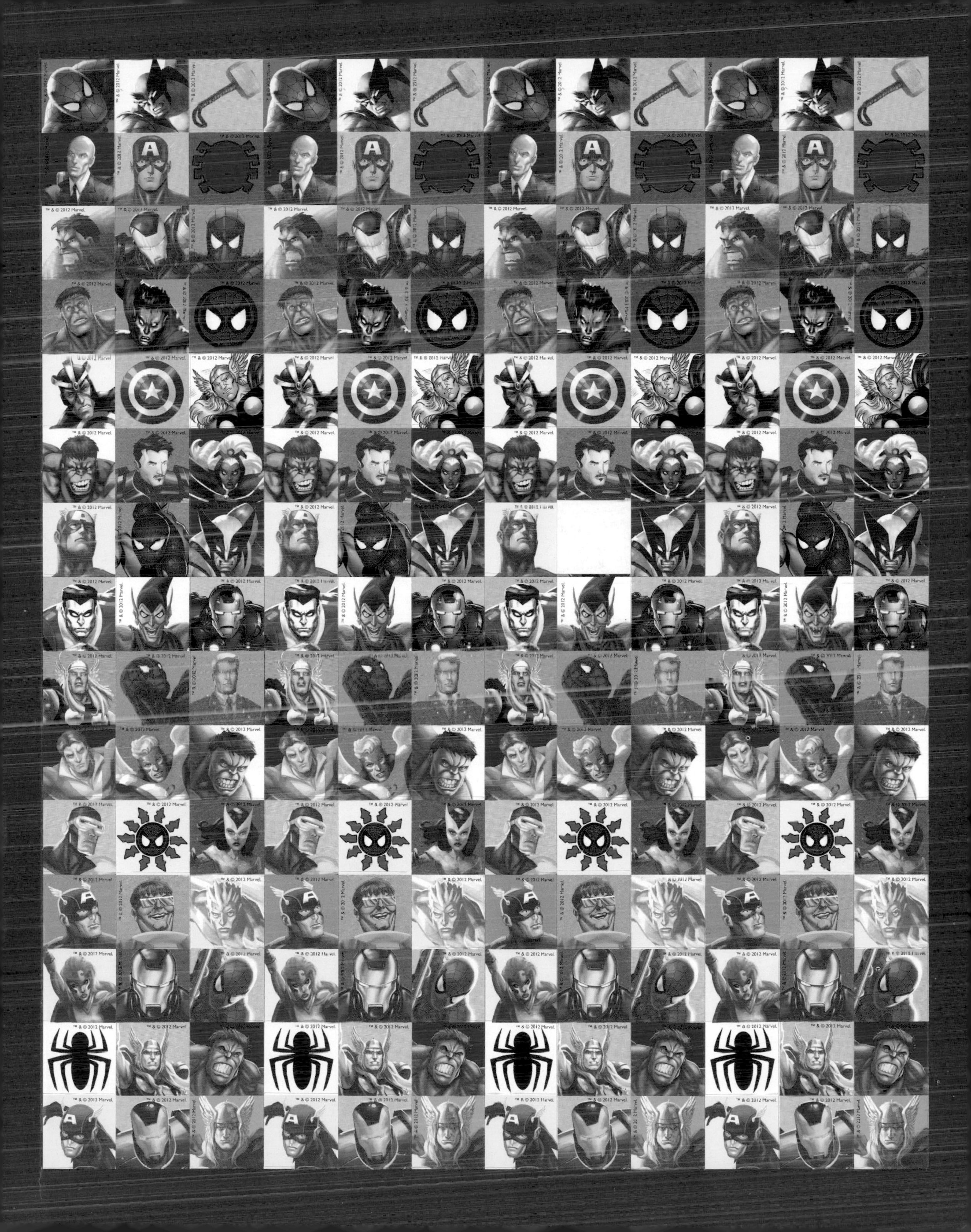
™ & © 2012 Marvel.

™ & © 2012 Marvel.

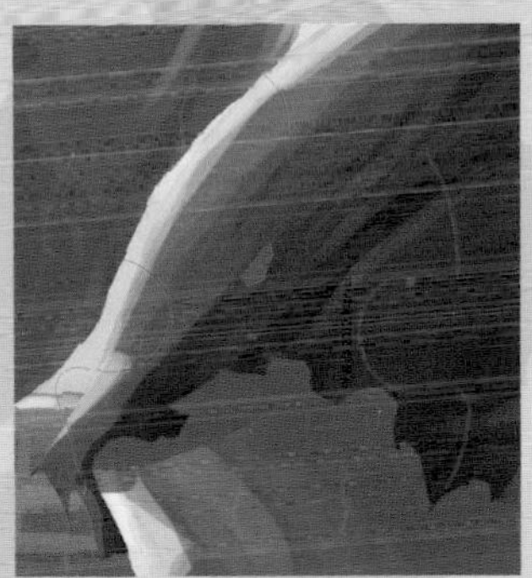

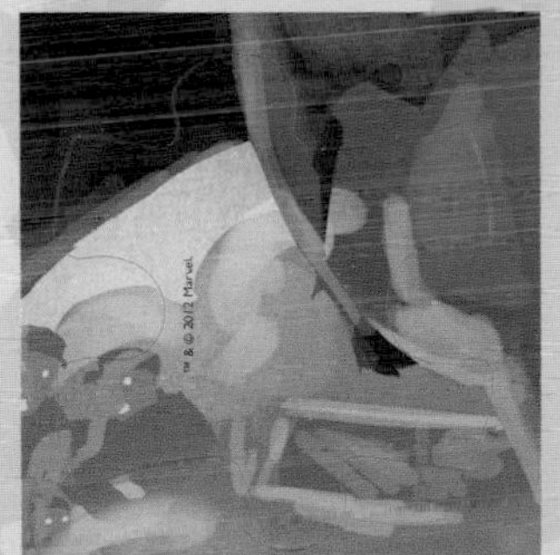

PAGE 37

PAGE 38

PAGE 39

PAGES 40-41

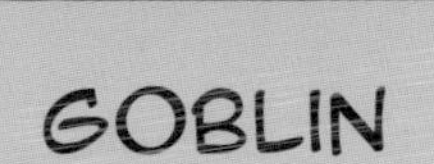

PEOPLE	HOORAY
LINE	GOBLIN
CHEERED	TRAIN
SPIDER-MAN	CHASED
TRACK	NEW YORK
CHASED	SPIDER-MAN
BRIDGE	WEBS

PAGES 42, 50 & 59

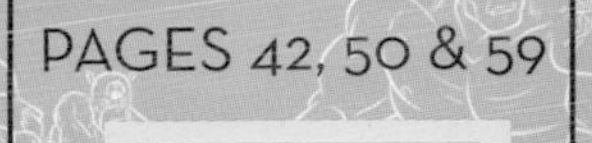

PAGE 44

PAGE 45

PAGE 46

PAGE 43

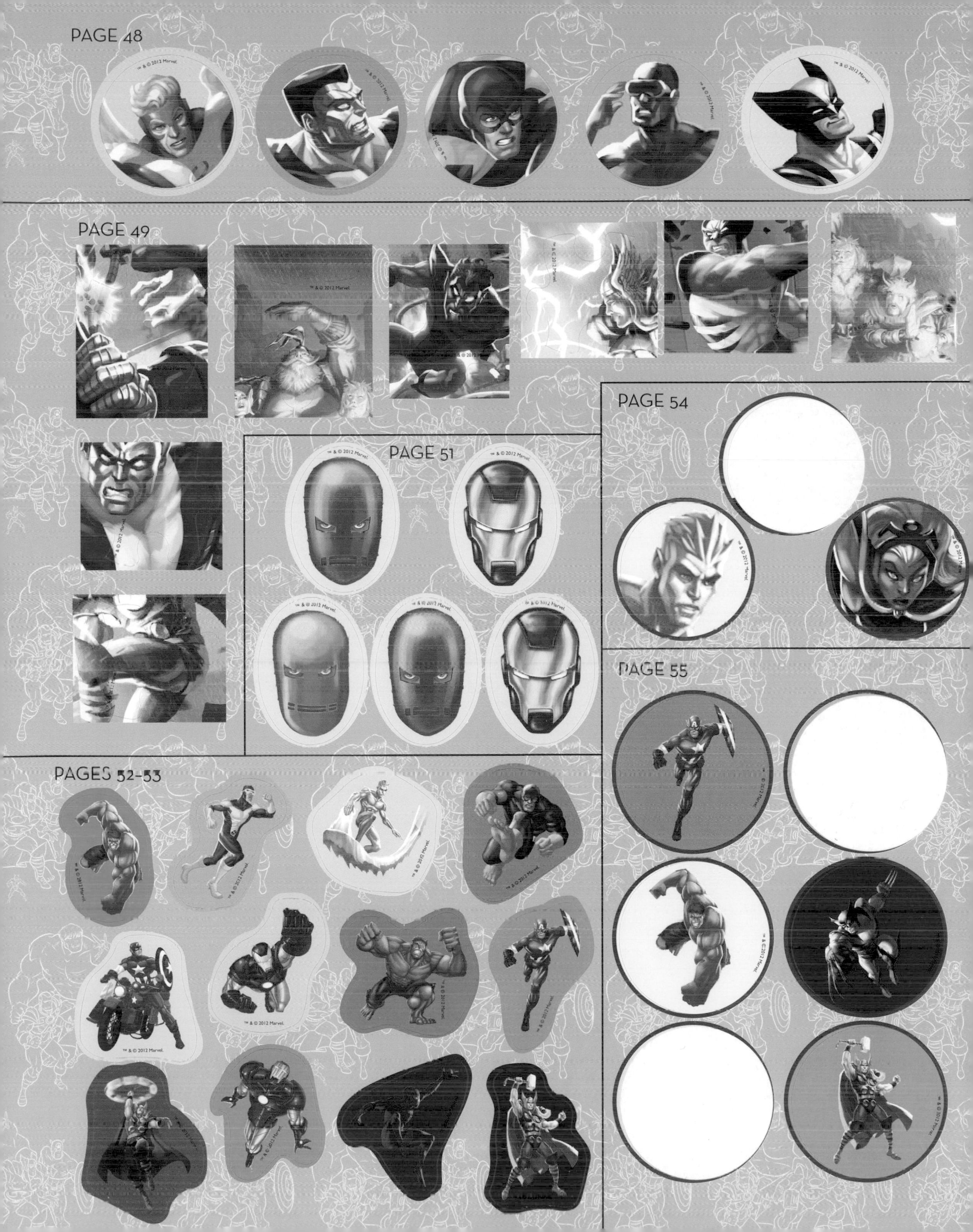
PAGE 48
PAGE 49
PAGE 51
PAGE 54
PAGE 55
PAGES 52–53
™ & © 2012 Marvel.

PAGE 56
PAGE 57
PAGE 58
PAGE 60
PAGE 61
PAGE 62
PAGE 63
™ & © 2012 Marvel.

1000 Stickers

Parragon

Bath • New York • Singapore • Hong Kong • Cologne • Delhi
Melbourne • Amsterdam • Johannesburg • Auckland • Shenzhen

First published by Parragon in 2012

Parragon
Chartist House
15-17 Trim Street
Bath BA1 1HA, UK
www.parragon.com

Edited by Sarah Mellowes
Production by Joanne Knowlson

ISBN 978-1-4454-7784-8

Printed in China

CONTENTS

COOL COLOURING

SHIELD OF POWER
Captain America to the rescue!

WATER PUNCH!
Spider-Man takes on Hydro-Man.

KA-BAAM!
Not even tanks can halt Hulk!

BLAST-OFF!
Iron Man's on a mission!

ROBO-DESTRUCTION
Wolverine rips into a robot!

HAMMER BLOW!
Thor takes on the mighty Storm Giant!

CRIME BUSTER!
Time to fight crime in New York City.

SMASHING!
Juggernaut unleashes some auto-chaos!

SPLASH-TASTIC!
Iron Man's just in time for a water rescue!

HERE COMES HULK!

Hulk leaps to repair a destroyed bridge.

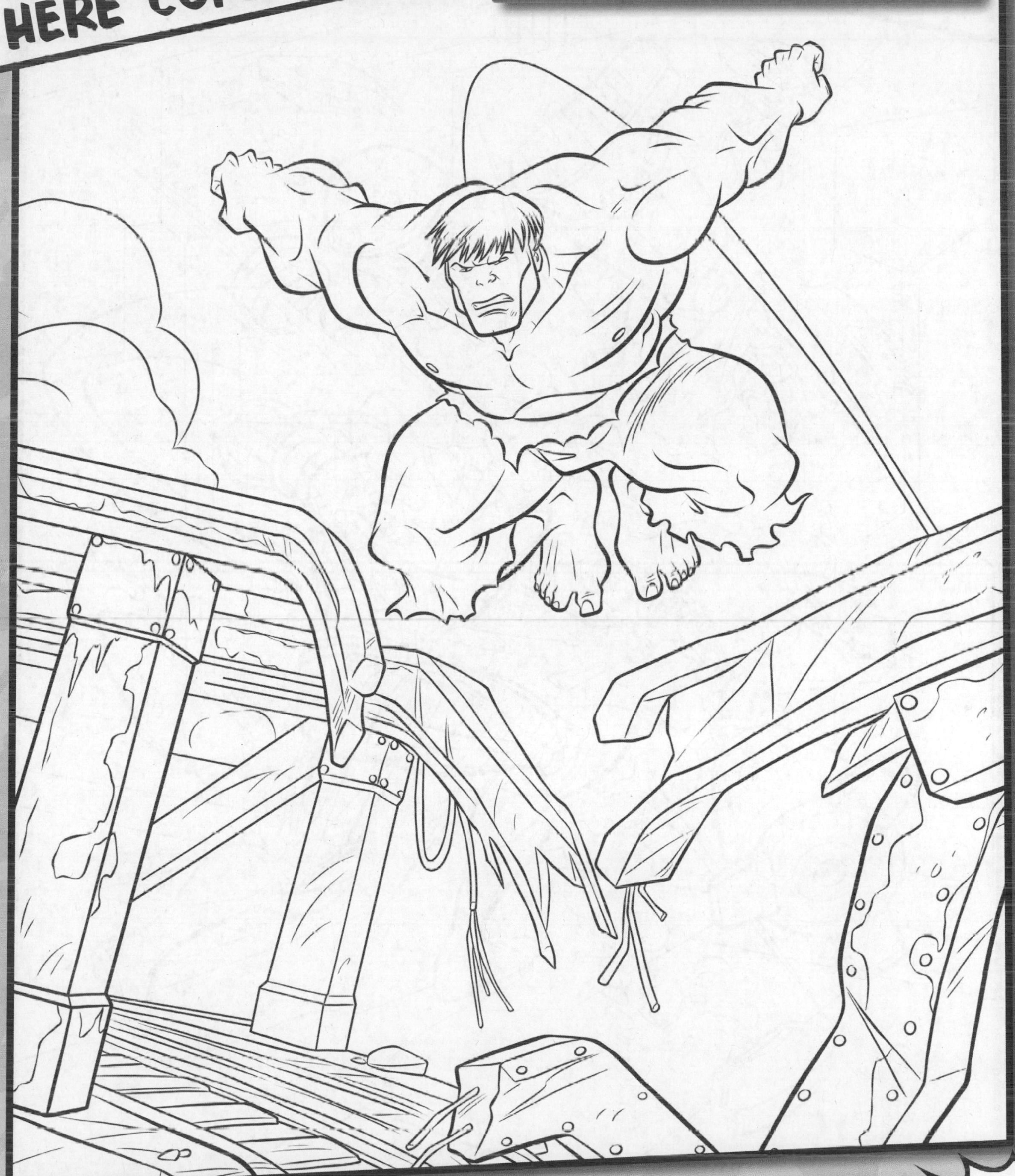

KNOCK KNOCK!
Colossus is coming in – ready or not!

ROBOT DEFLECTOR

Captain America battles the Alpha-Bot.

STARK CHANGE
So long, Tony Stark. Hello, Iron Man!

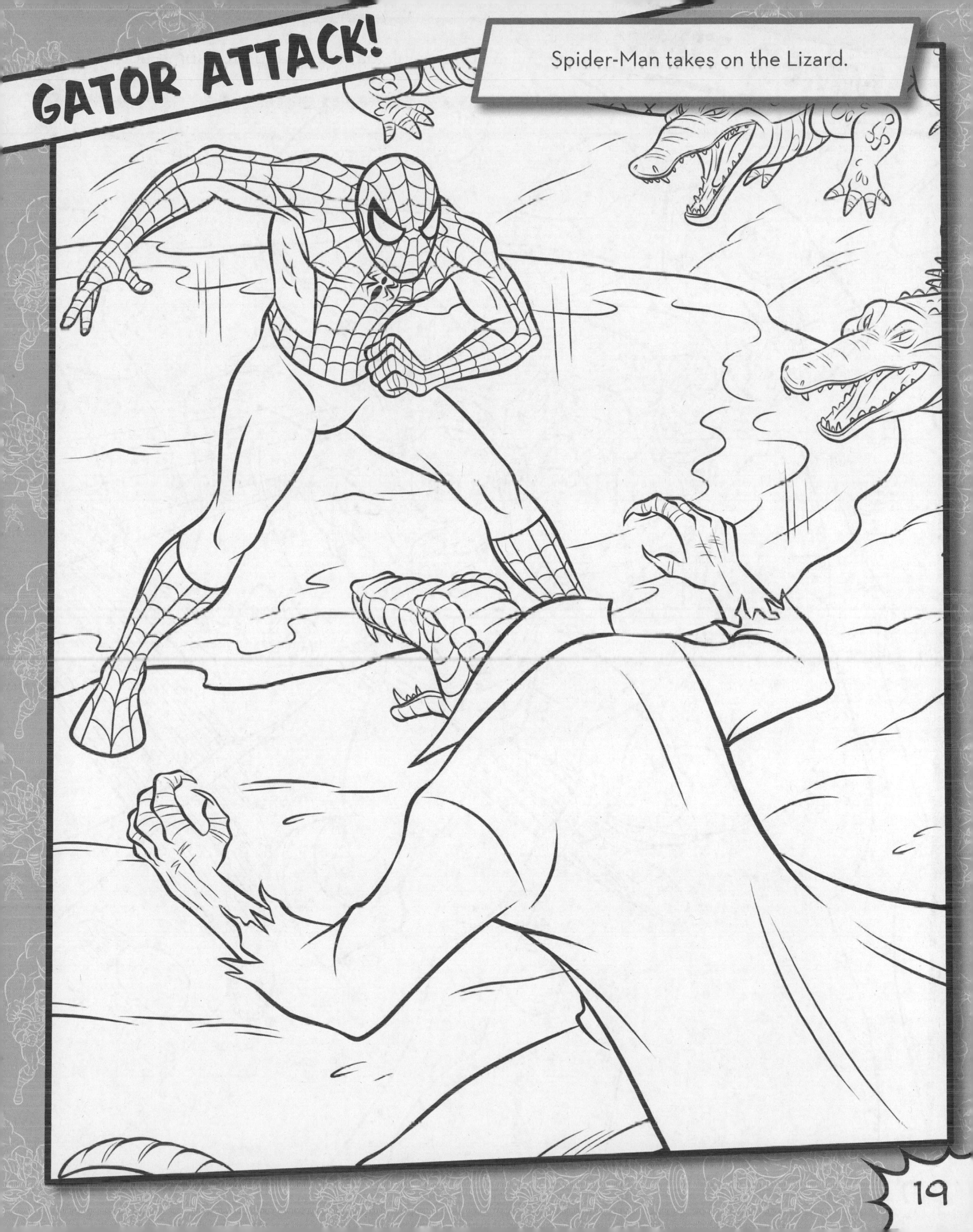
GATOR ATTACK!
Spider-Man takes on the Lizard.

HAMMER TIME!
Thor gets his hammer ready for some action!

GREEN ENVY
From Bruce Banner to the Incredible Hulk!

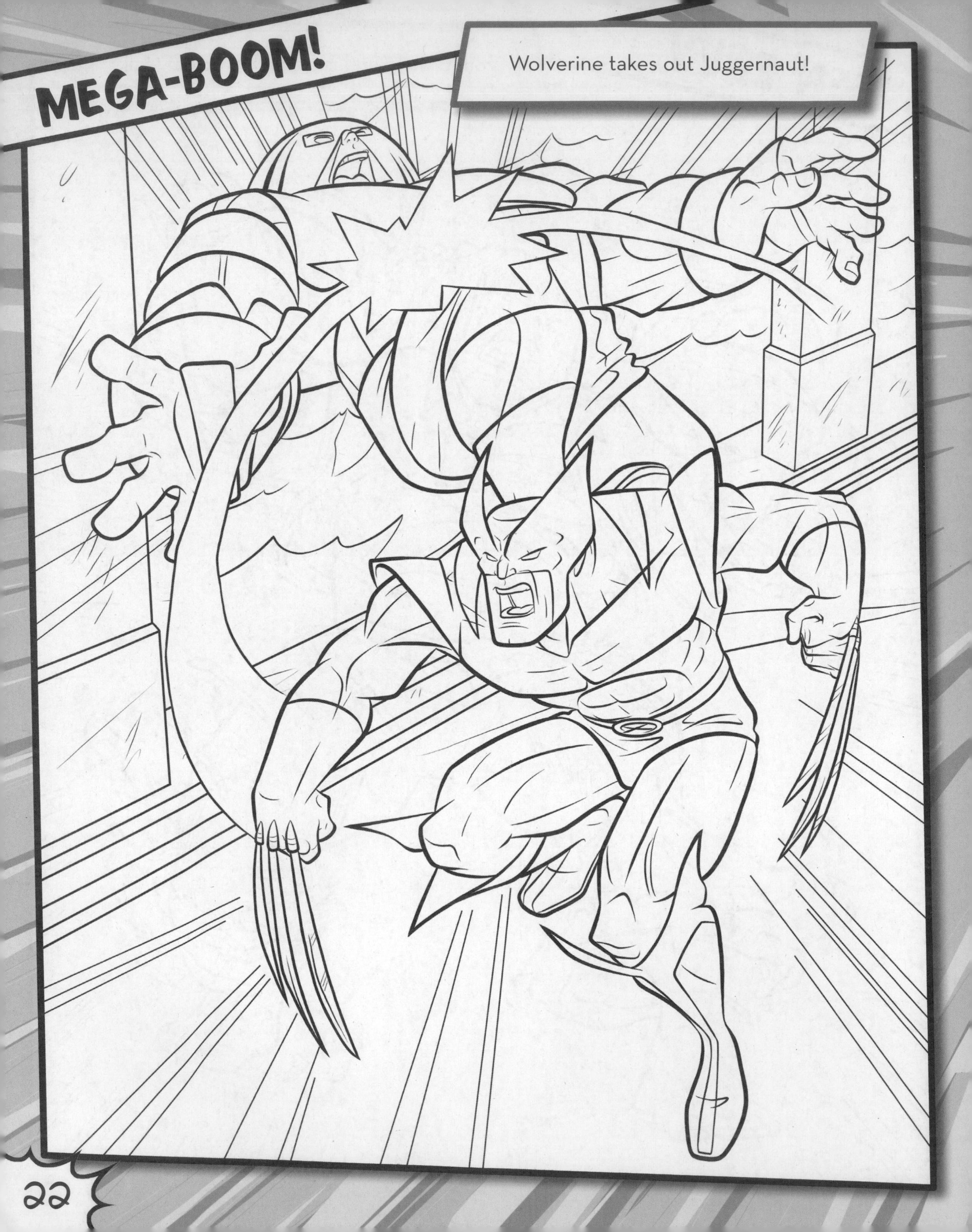
MEGA-BOOM!
Wolverine takes out Juggernaut!

SECONDS AWAY
Can the X-Men stop Arcade's countdown?
0:02

GIANT HAND
Captain America gets a helping hand from Giant Man.

BACK TO BASICS!
Time to get back to Peter Parker!

SO LONG, FOLKS!
Iron Man heads for home after
another amazing day.

FOREVER BANISHED
Thor banishes his evil brother to the Island of the Trolls.

GOOD JOB!
Spider-Man makes short work of Electro.

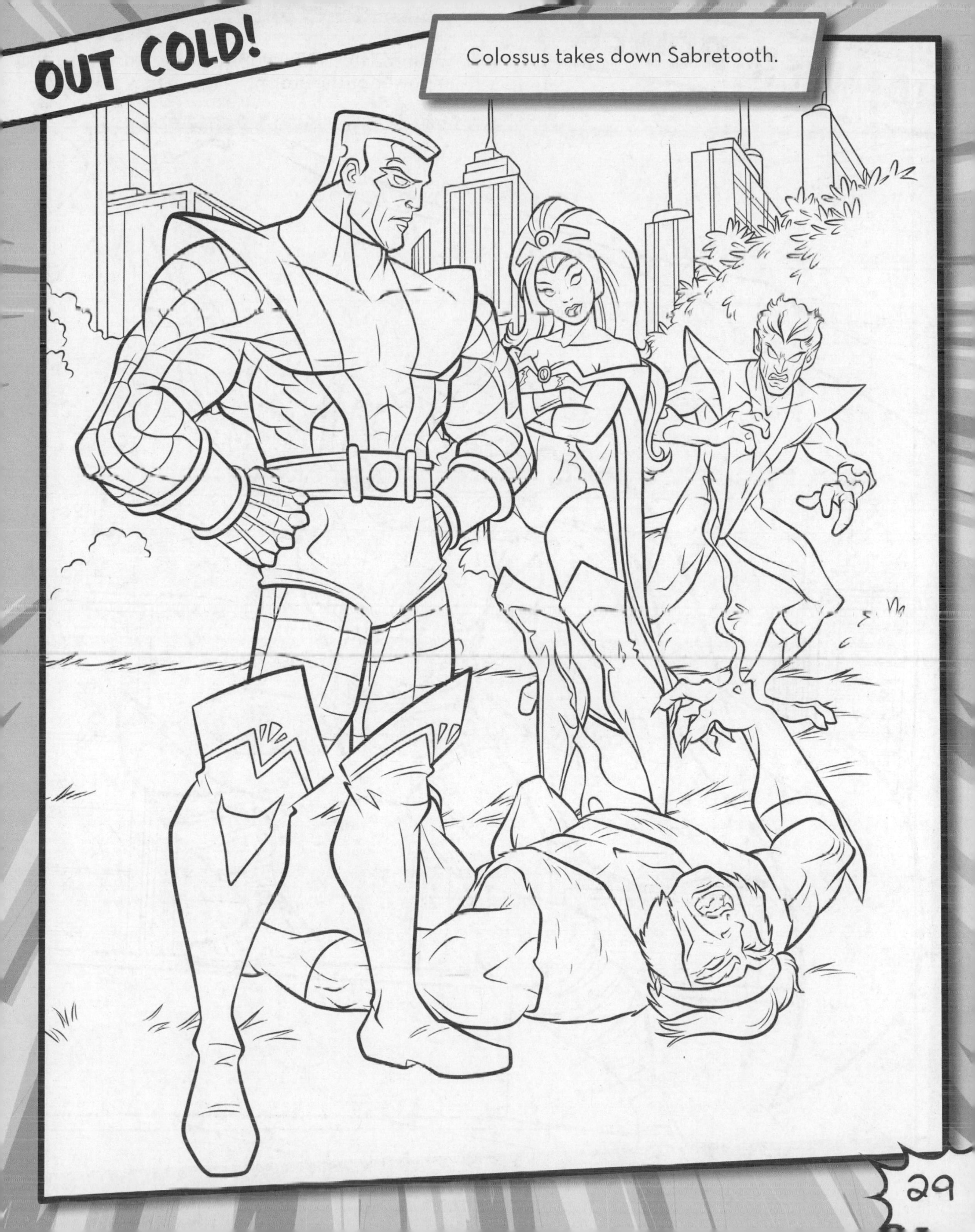
OUT COLD!
Colossus takes down Sabretooth.

HAMMER POWER
The Mighty Thor commands
the power of the storm!

SURPRISE GUEST!
"Surprise, surprise, Controller!"

BOT BOWLING!
Hulk goes crimebot bowling!

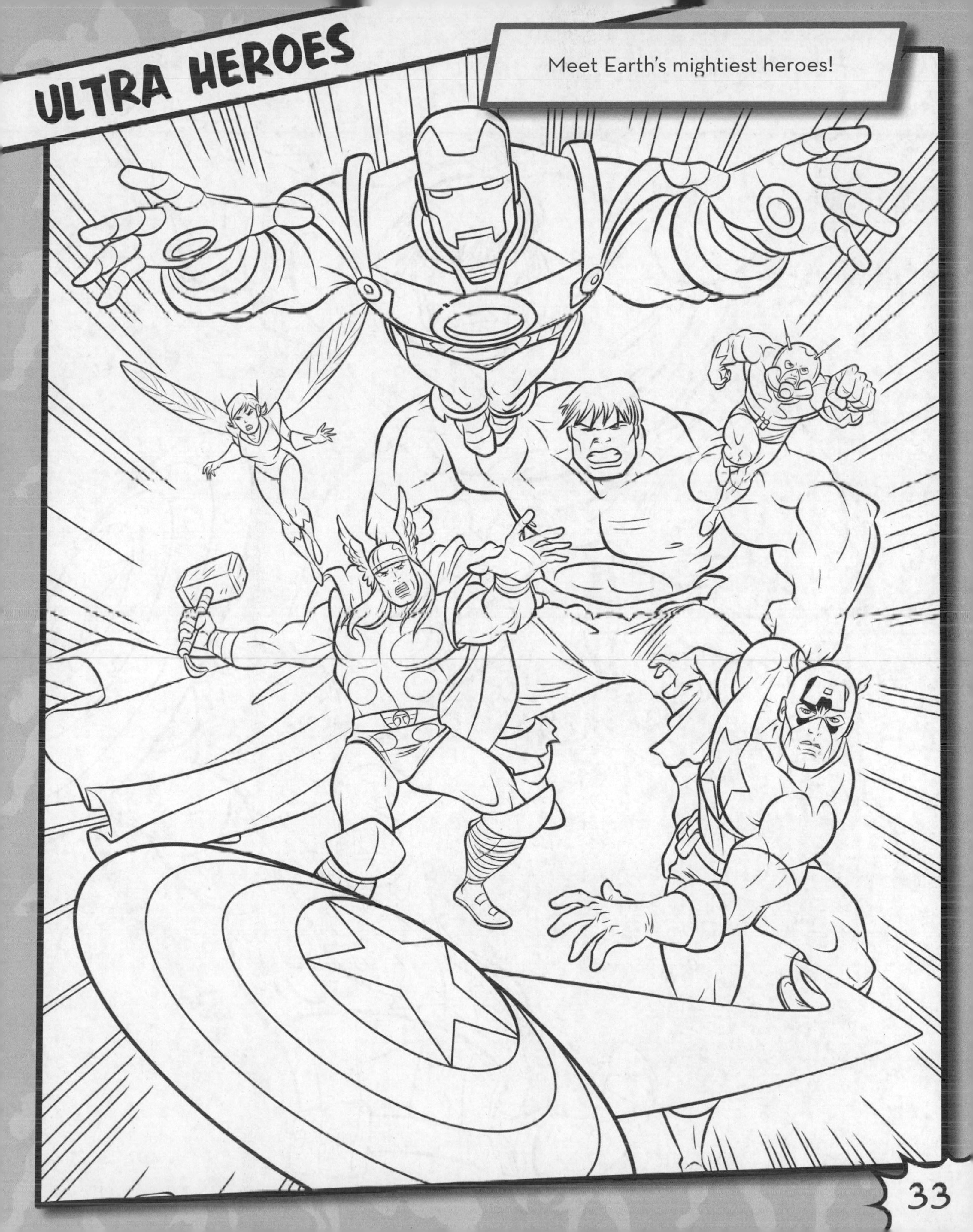
ULTRA HEROES
Meet Earth's mightiest heroes!

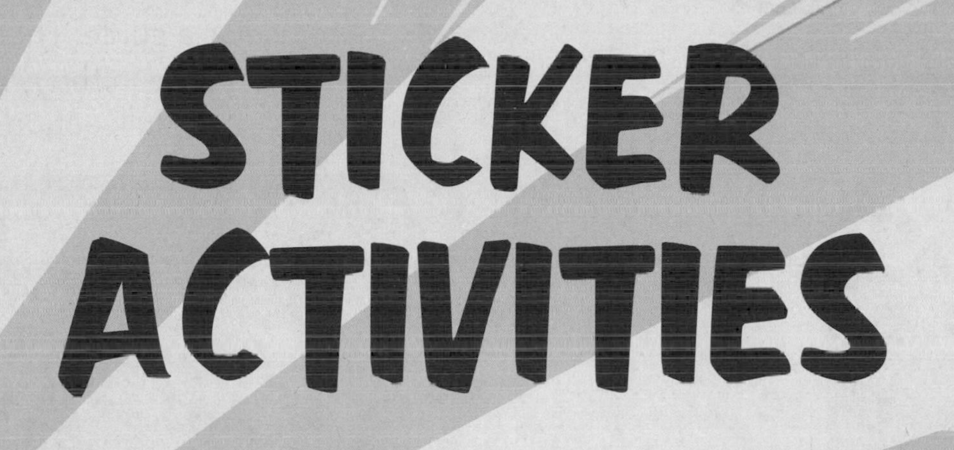
STICKER
ACTIVITIES

SMASHING PUZZLE

Place the larger sticker from your sticker sheet into the rectangle below to use as a guide. Then arrange the puzzle pieces in the grid to complete this Hulk action scene!

MISSING IN ACTION!

Some of your favourite heroes are missing in action! Find the correct stickers to complete the pictures so they can defeat their enemies.

TRAINING SEQUENCES

Can you work out which picture comes next in each sequence? Use your stickers to complete the patterns.

CLUE TO A HERO

Read the clues and then add the correct stickers to reveal the heroes.

1. THIS POWERFUL WARRIOR WAS CAST OUT OF ASGARD AND SENT TO LIVE WITH HUMANS ON EARTH. ?

2. LOGAN UNDERGOES A MUTATION TO JOIN THE X-MEN AND TAKES ON HIS NEW POWERFUL FORM. ?

3. THIS WEALTHY INDUSTRIALIST IS FORCED TO BUILD AN ARMOURED SUIT TO FIGHT AGAINST EVIL. ?

4. THIS INCREDIBLE HERO STUDIED A TYPE OF GAMMA RADIATION TO USE ITS POWER FOR GOOD. ?

5. HE WAS NOT FIT ENOUGH TO JOIN THE ARMY BUT SIGNED UP FOR A CLASSIFIED 'REBIRTH' PROJECT. ?

SPIDER-MAN ADVENTURE

Use the word stickers on your sticker sheets to complete this spectacular Spider-Man story!

IT WAS A COLD NIGHT IN

THE CITY AND TROUBLE

WAS IN THE AIR.

[ ] HAD

ALREADY BEEN HARD AT

WORK. A [ ]

HAD COLLAPSED AND HE HAD TO USE [ ] TO REBUILD

THE [ ] BEFORE THE SPEEDING [ ]

PLUMMETED OVER THE EDGE. AS SOON AS THE TRAIN WAS

SAVED, THE GREEN [ ] SUDDENLY APPEARED.

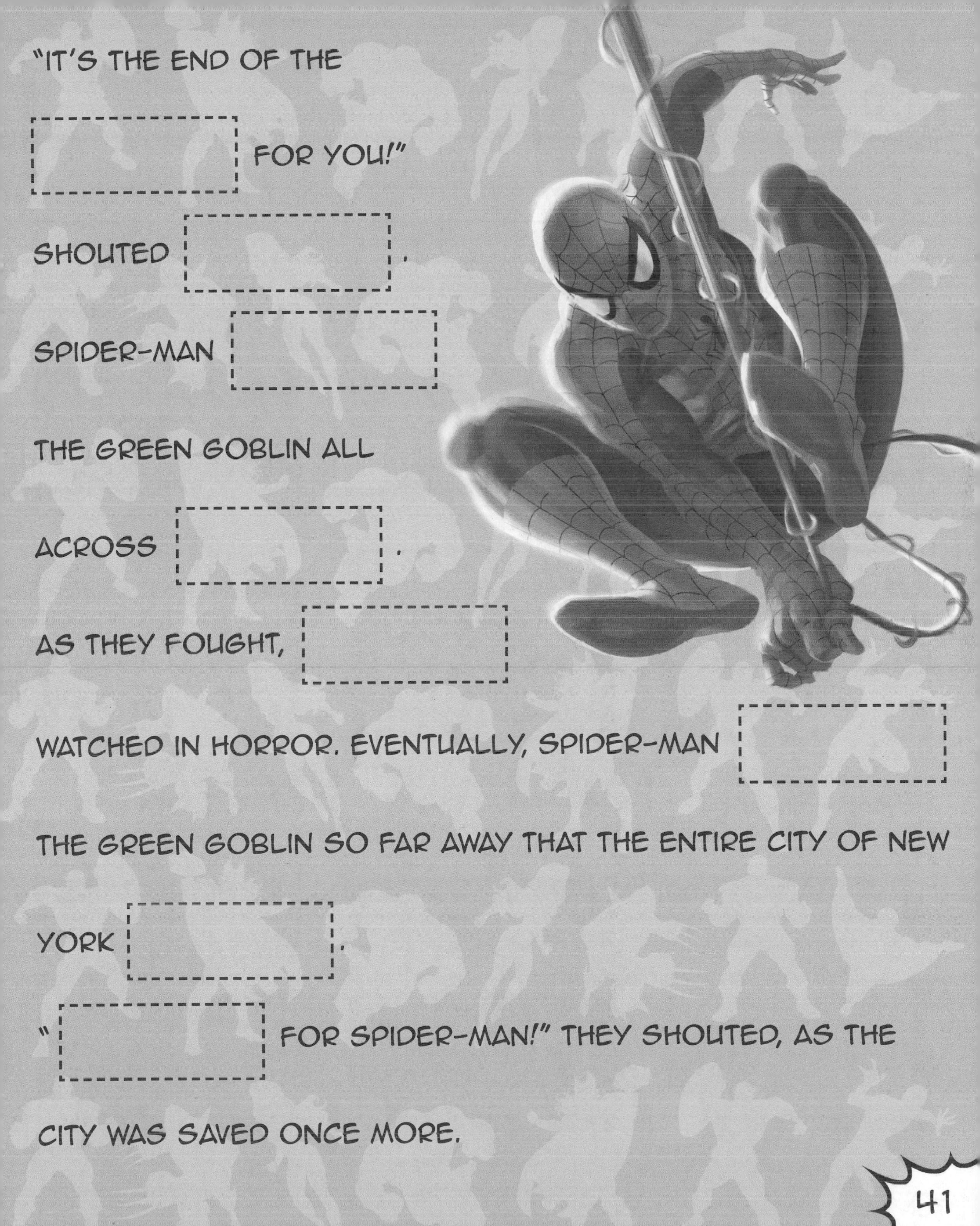

"IT'S THE END OF THE

[ ] FOR YOU!"

SHOUTED [ ].

SPIDER-MAN [ ]

THE GREEN GOBLIN ALL

ACROSS [ ].

AS THEY FOUGHT, [ ]

WATCHED IN HORROR. EVENTUALLY, SPIDER-MAN [ ]

THE GREEN GOBLIN SO FAR AWAY THAT THE ENTIRE CITY OF NEW

YORK [ ].

" [ ] FOR SPIDER-MAN!" THEY SHOUTED, AS THE

CITY WAS SAVED ONCE MORE.

ODD SPIDEY OUT!

The web-slinging wonder swings across the city! All these pictures are identical except one. Can you find the odd one out and place your 'tick' sticker onto the picture?

IRON MAN ACTION!

Place the larger sticker from your sticker sheet into the rectangle below to use as a guide. Then arrange the puzzle pieces in the grid to complete this amazing Iron Man scene!

HERO IDENTITIES

How well do you know your super heroes? Find the stickers to reveal the secret identities of the two super heroes below.

1

HE VOWED TO PROTECT JUSTICE, EQUALITY AND FREEDOM.

HIS REAL NAME WHEN HE'S NOT A SUPER HERO IS STEVE ROGERS.

THIS AMERICAN HERO WAS PRESENTED WITH A SPECIAL SHIELD.

?

2

THIS SUPER HERO WAS NOT ALWAYS ABLE TO DO INCREDIBLE THINGS.

HE WORKED FOR THE ARMY AS A DOCTOR OF SCIENCE.

ENERGY RADIATION CHANGED HIM AND GAVE HIM SUPER STRENGTH.

?

VANISHING X-MEN!

Complete this all-action X-Men scene with your stickers, as they fight for the good of humanity!

MAN TO HERO

Help the Hulk turn back into Bruce Banner without causing any more destruction! Once you've found the correct trail, add stickers to their shadows.

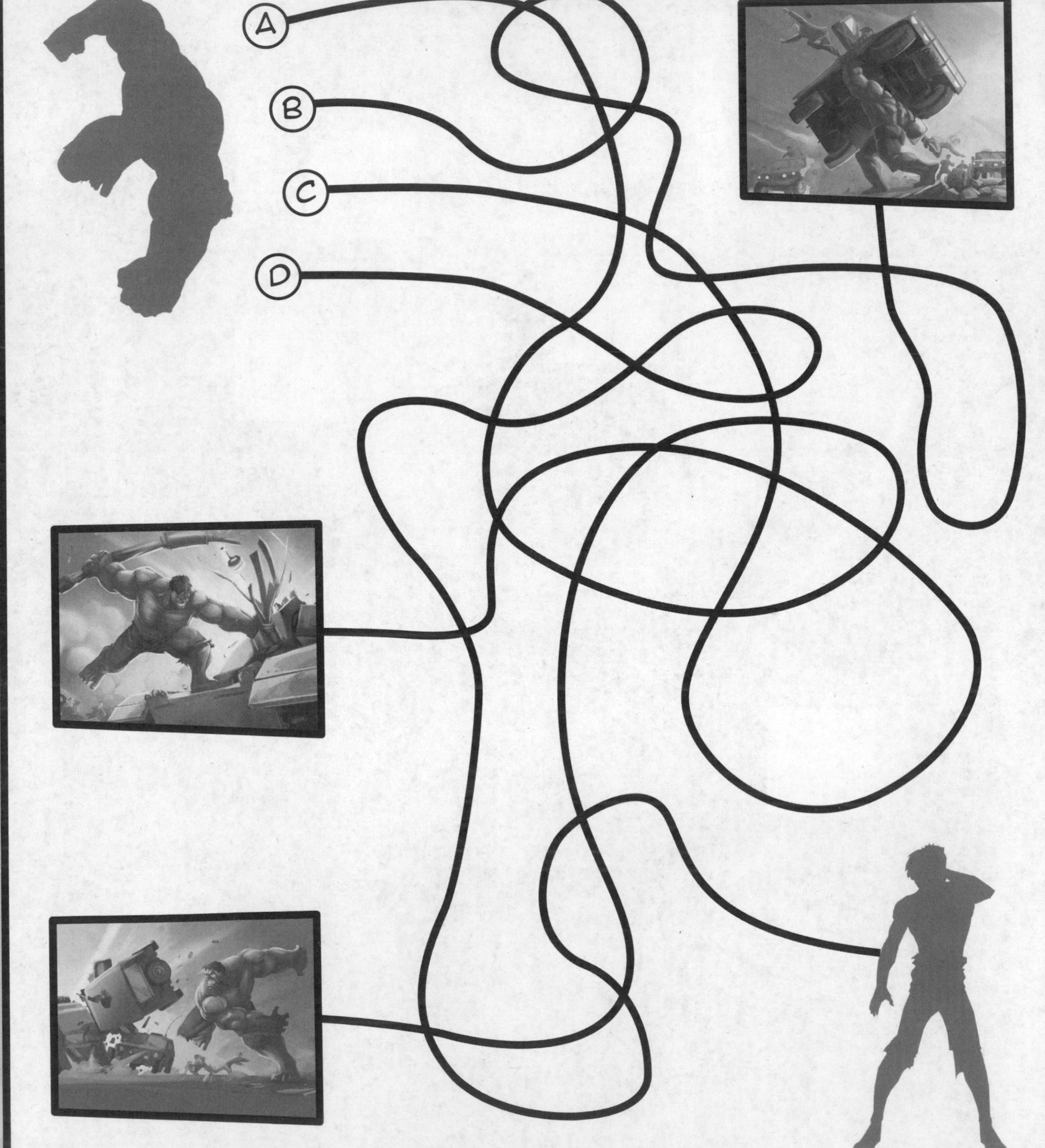

SUPER SUDOKU!

Complete these super Sudoku puzzles with your stickers. Each row, column and box must contain one of each of the six stickers.

X-MEN STICKERS

Each member of the X-Men has a special power. Can you match the correct sticker to each character description?

PIECE OF THE ACTION

Check out the super heroes in action! Find the correct sticker pieces to complete these battle scenes.

ODD CAPTAIN OUT

Captain America is helping his country win the worldwide war! All of these pictures are the same except one. Can you find the odd one out and place your 'tick' sticker next to the picture?

MASK SEQUENCES

Can you work out which mask comes next in each sequence? Use your stickers to complete the patterns.

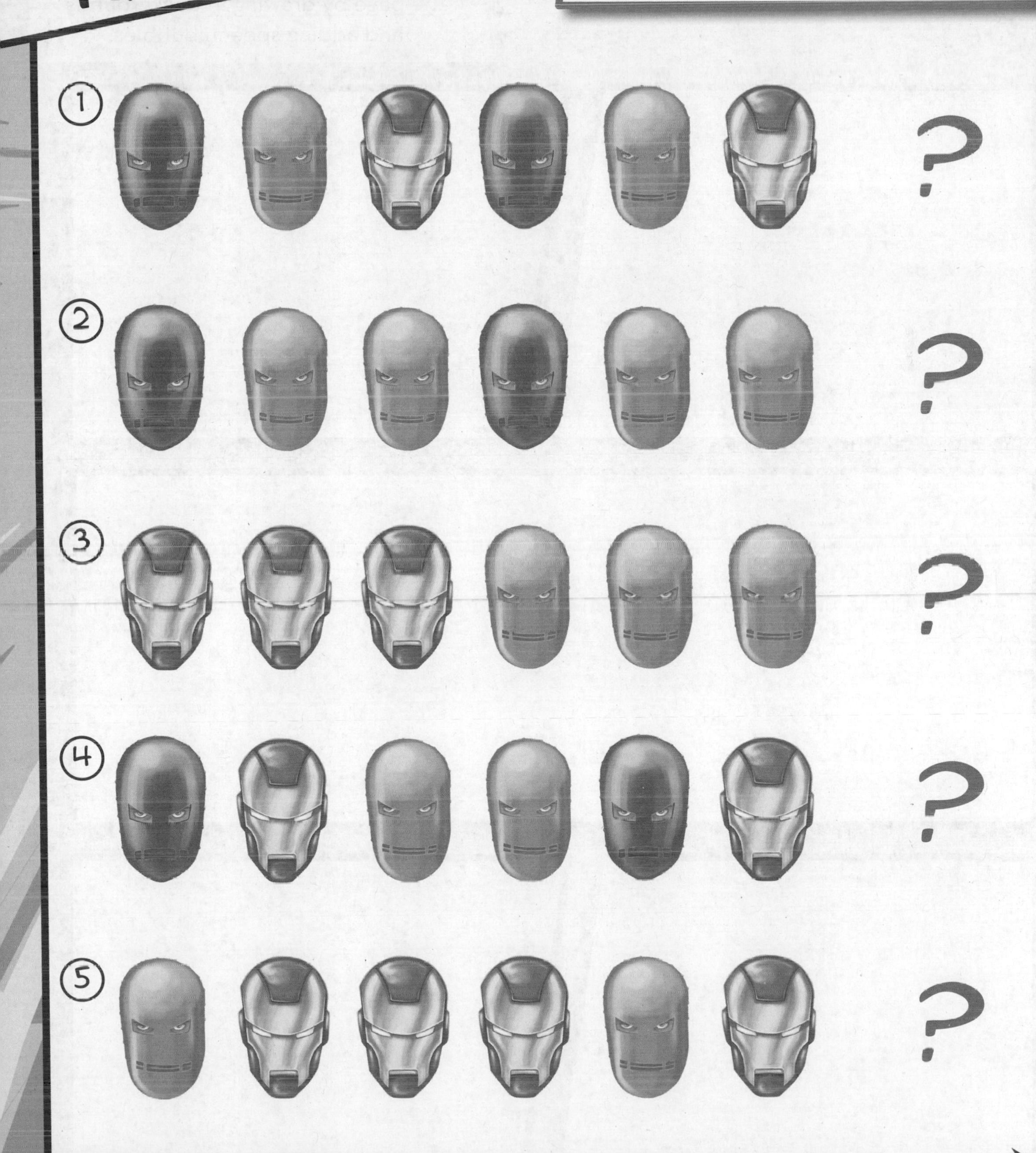

COMIC BOOK CREATOR

Use your stickers to create your own awesome hero adventure in the comic strip below. Make the action jump off the page by drawing in backgrounds and adding speech bubbles.

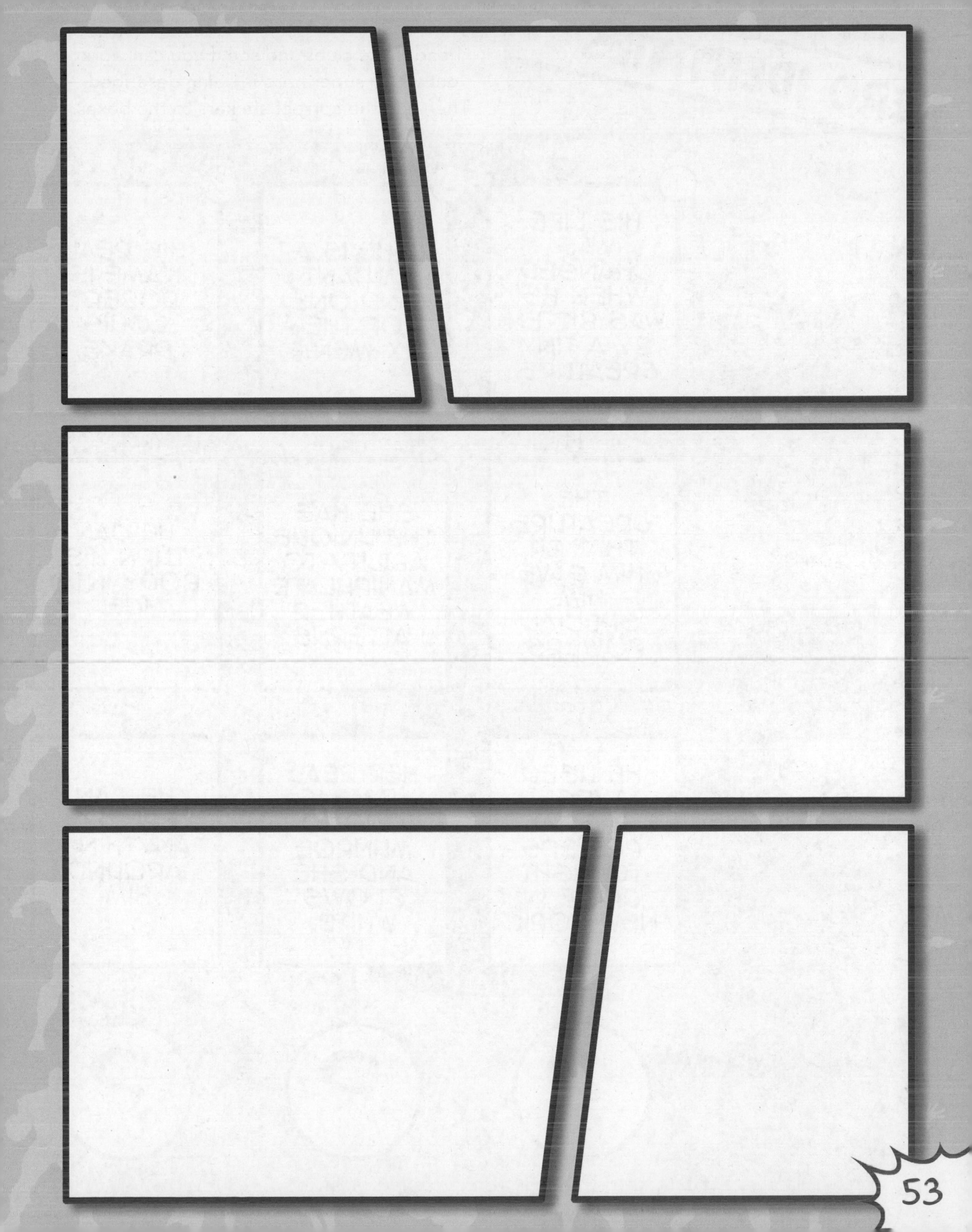

HERO IDENTITIES

Read these clues and see if you can work out which super hero is being described. Then add the correct stickers to the boxes.

HERO SHADOWS
Put your super hero powers to the test!
Find the super hero stickers that correctly
match the hero shadows below.
A
B
C
D
E
F

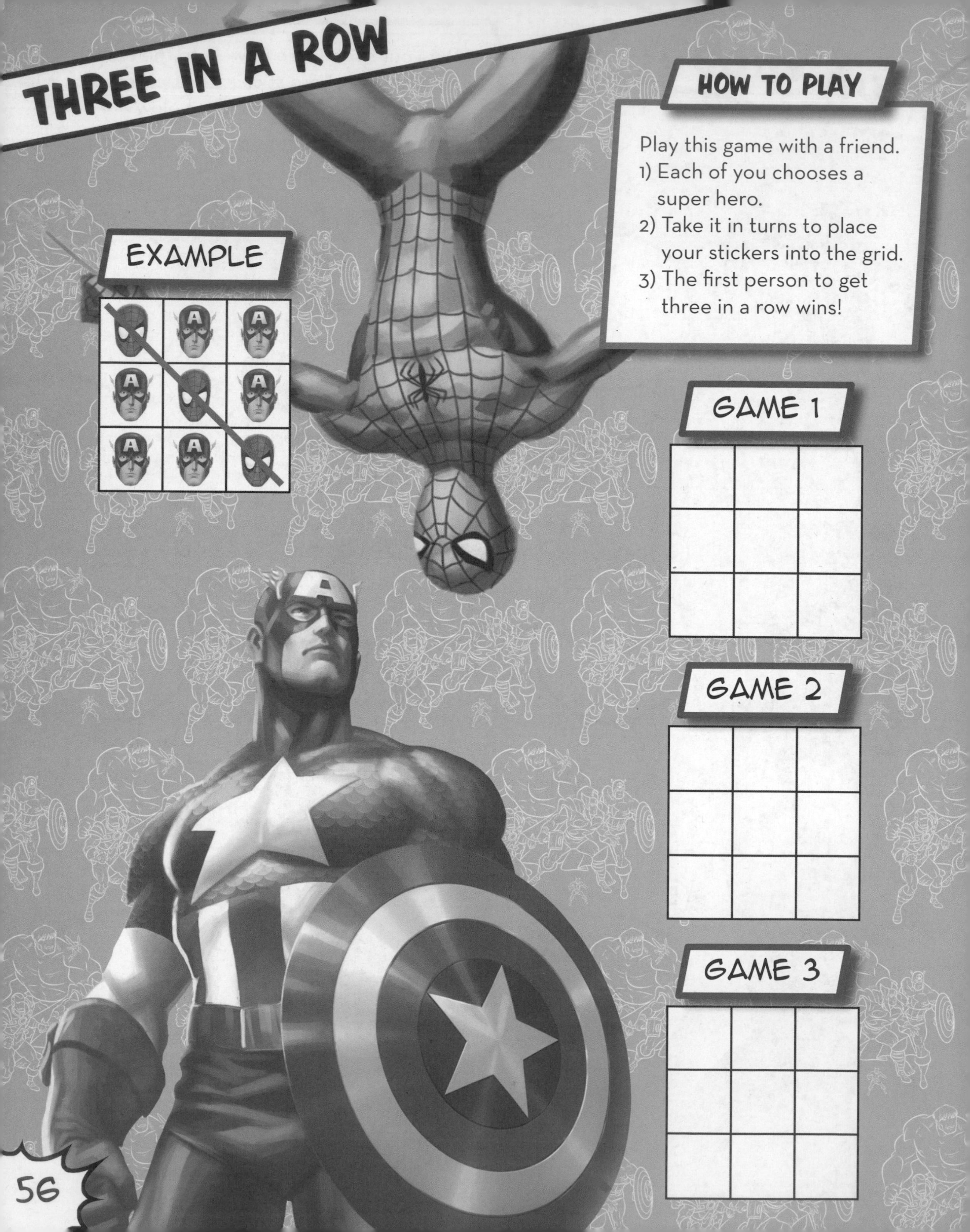
THREE IN A ROW
EXAMPLE
HOW TO PLAY
Play this game with a friend.
1) Each of you chooses a super hero.
2) Take it in turns to place your stickers into the grid.
3) The first person to get three in a row wins!
GAME 1
GAME 2
GAME 3

LET'S GET CLOSER

Work out which hero is in each close-up. Then place the correct sticker next to each hero.

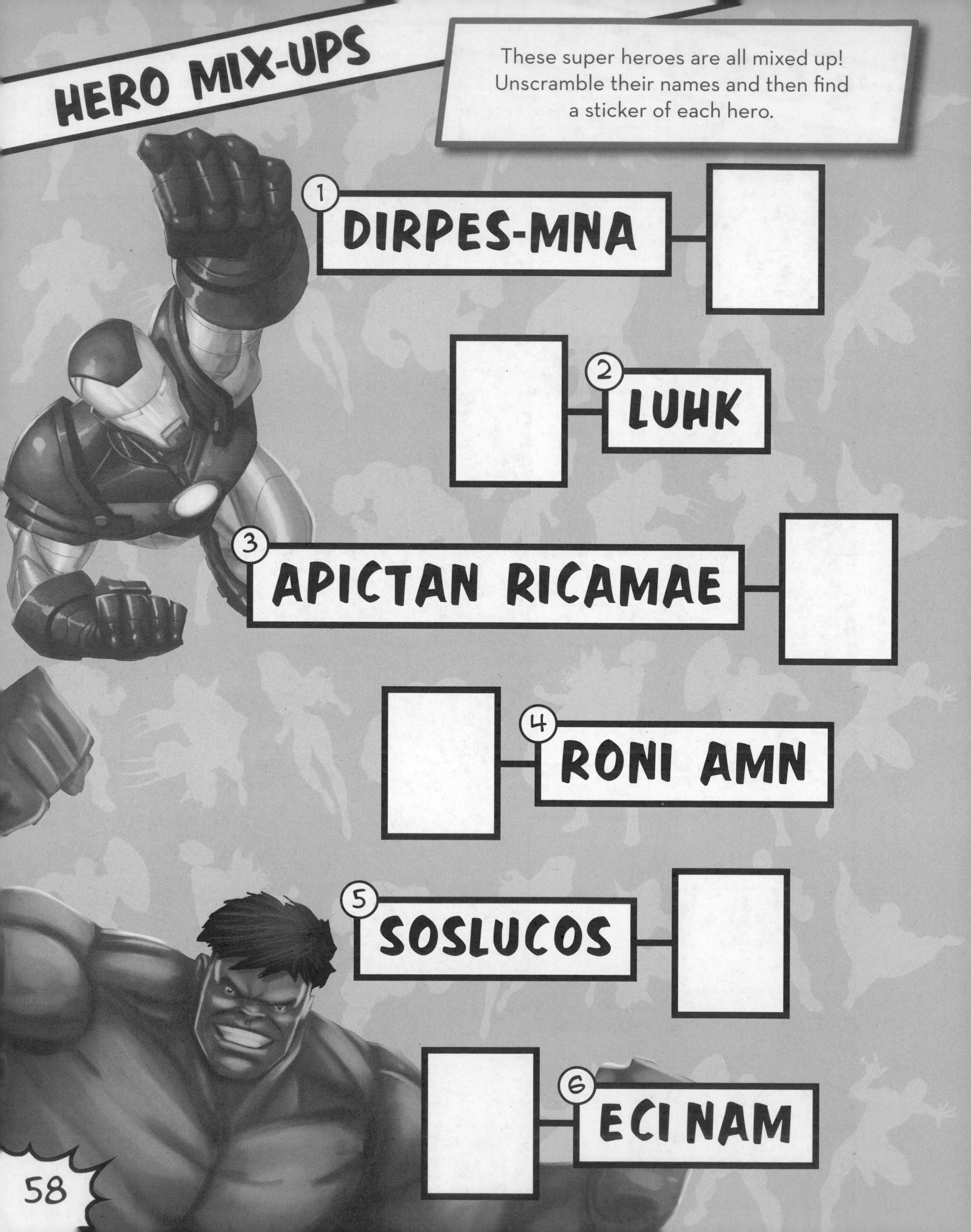

HERO MIX-UPS

These super heroes are all mixed up! Unscramble their names and then find a sticker of each hero.

1. DIRPES-MNA
2. LUHK
3. APICTAN RICAMAE
4. RONI AMN
5. SOSLUCOS
6. ECI NAM

SPIDEY PAIRS

There are eight pictures of Spider-Man below, but only two are exactly the same. Place your 'tick' stickers onto the two pictures that match exactly.

A

B

C

D

E

F

G

H

THOR SUDOKU

Complete this super Sudoku puzzle with your stickers. Each row, column and box must contain one of each of the six stickers.

THE X-TRAIL

Help Professor X reach Wolverine. Once you've found the correct trail, add stickers to their shadows.

A

B

C

INCREDIBLE JIGSAWS

The Hulk is releasing his rage! Find the correct stickers to complete these all-action scenes.

IRON DESTRUCTION

Complete this explosive Iron Man scene with your stickers, as he fights evil robots!

ACTIVITY ACTION

TRAPPED!

Can you join the dots to help Polaris trap Toad? Then colour the scene!

BACK HOME!

Which path will lead the Avengers home to Earth?

START

A B C D E F G

FINISH

IRON GRID

Copy this picture of Iron Man into the grid below. Then colour him in before he soars into action!

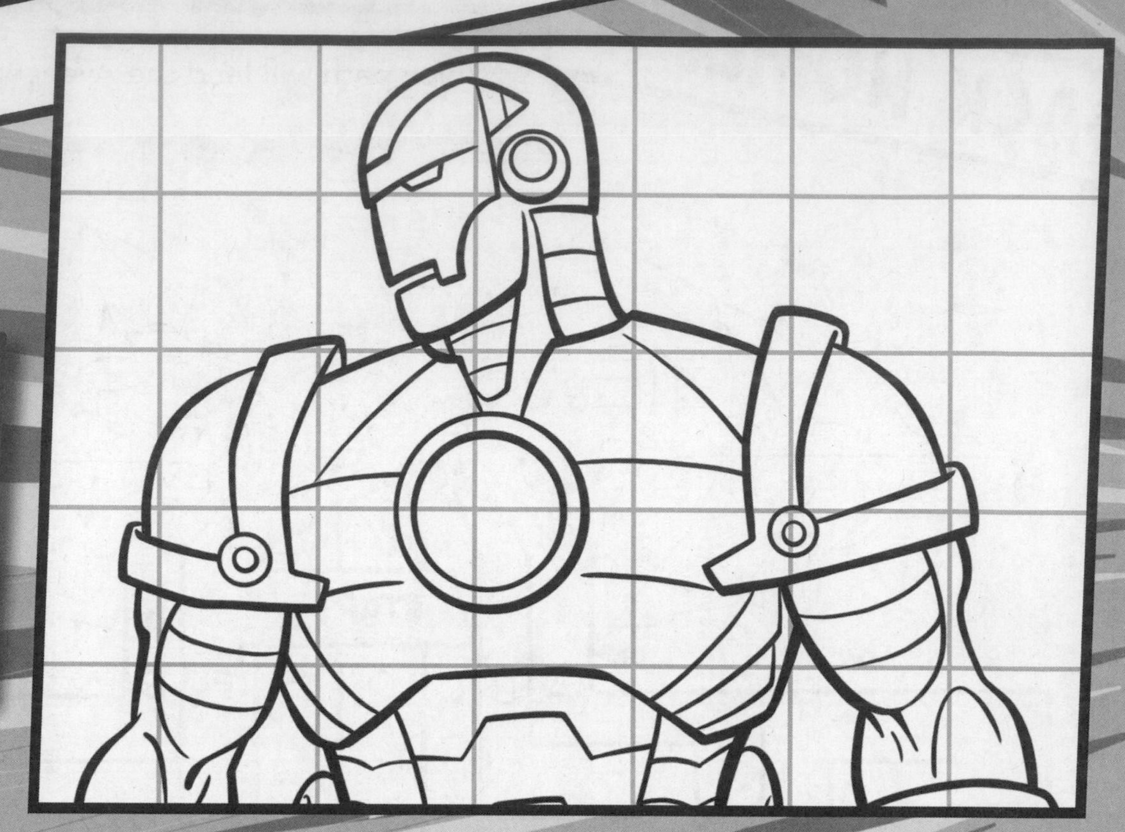

POWER MATCH

Put your X-Men powers to the test! Draw a line to match each of the X-Men to their power or weapon.

ALTER-EGO!

Spidey is on a mission! Can you spot five differences in the bottom picture?

MYSTERY HERO

Complete the crossword to discover the mystery hero.

1. HEROES OFTEN HIDE THEIR FACE WITH A... .
2. CAPTAIN AMERICA HOLDS A... .
3. THE HULK'S SKIN IS... .
4. THOR'S WEAPON IS A... .
5. PROFESSOR XAVIER'S TEAM ARE CALLED THE X-... .

NAME SUDOKU

Use the letters in the names WASP and HULK to complete the grids. Each letter can only appear once in every row, column and large square.

WASP

W	A	S	P
S			
	W		
			A

HULK

H			K
	K		
U			L
		H	

WEAPON CHAOS
How many hammers and swords can you count in the jumble below?
Write your answers here.
73

WEB TRAIL

Spidey's chasing down a bad guy!
Which web trail will catch the evil Electro?

A
B
C
D
E

RHINO

KA-ZOOM!

Get closer to the super heroes! Look at these extreme close-ups and work out which hero is in each picture.

1. IRON MAN
2. CAPTAIN AMERICA
3. ANTMAN
4. SPIDER-MAN
5. HULK
6. WOLVERINE

A

B

C
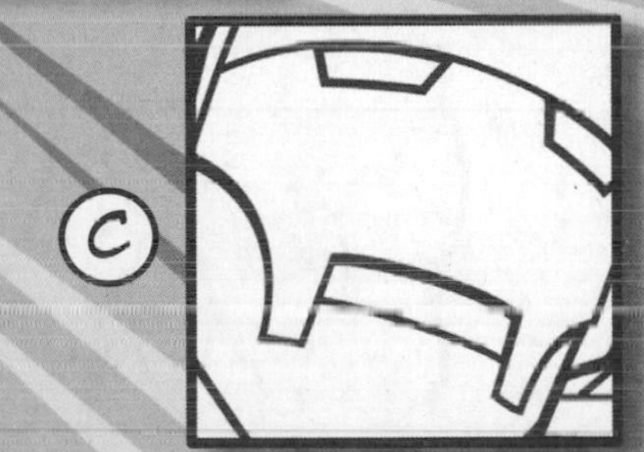

D
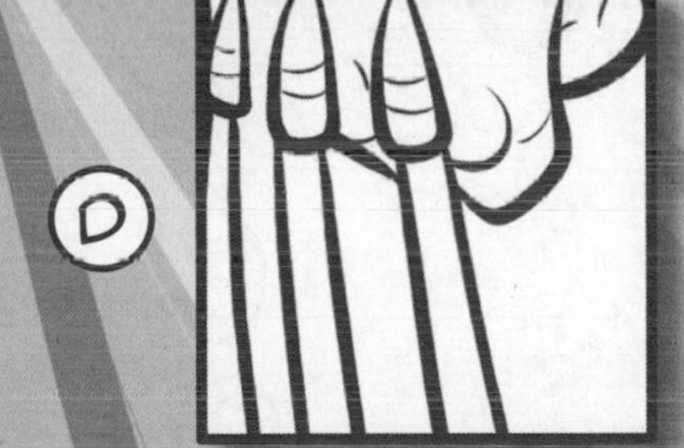

E

F

IN THE SHADOWS

Captain America strikes in battle!
Which of these shadows is the exact match
for Captain America?

GUESS WHO?

Unscramble the word below to discover the X-Men hero.

LOVEWINER

MEMORY POWER

Get your super powers at the ready to play this memory game with a friend!

HOW TO PLAY

1) Cover up each super hero with a square of paper.
2) Take it in turns to uncover two heroes at a time. Try to get a matching pair!
3) If you don't reveal a matching pair, cover up the super heroes again. If you reveal a matching pair then keep the two squares of paper.
4) Whoever has the most squares of paper once all the super heroes are revealed wins!

WHO'S NEXT?

Can you work out who comes next in each sequence?

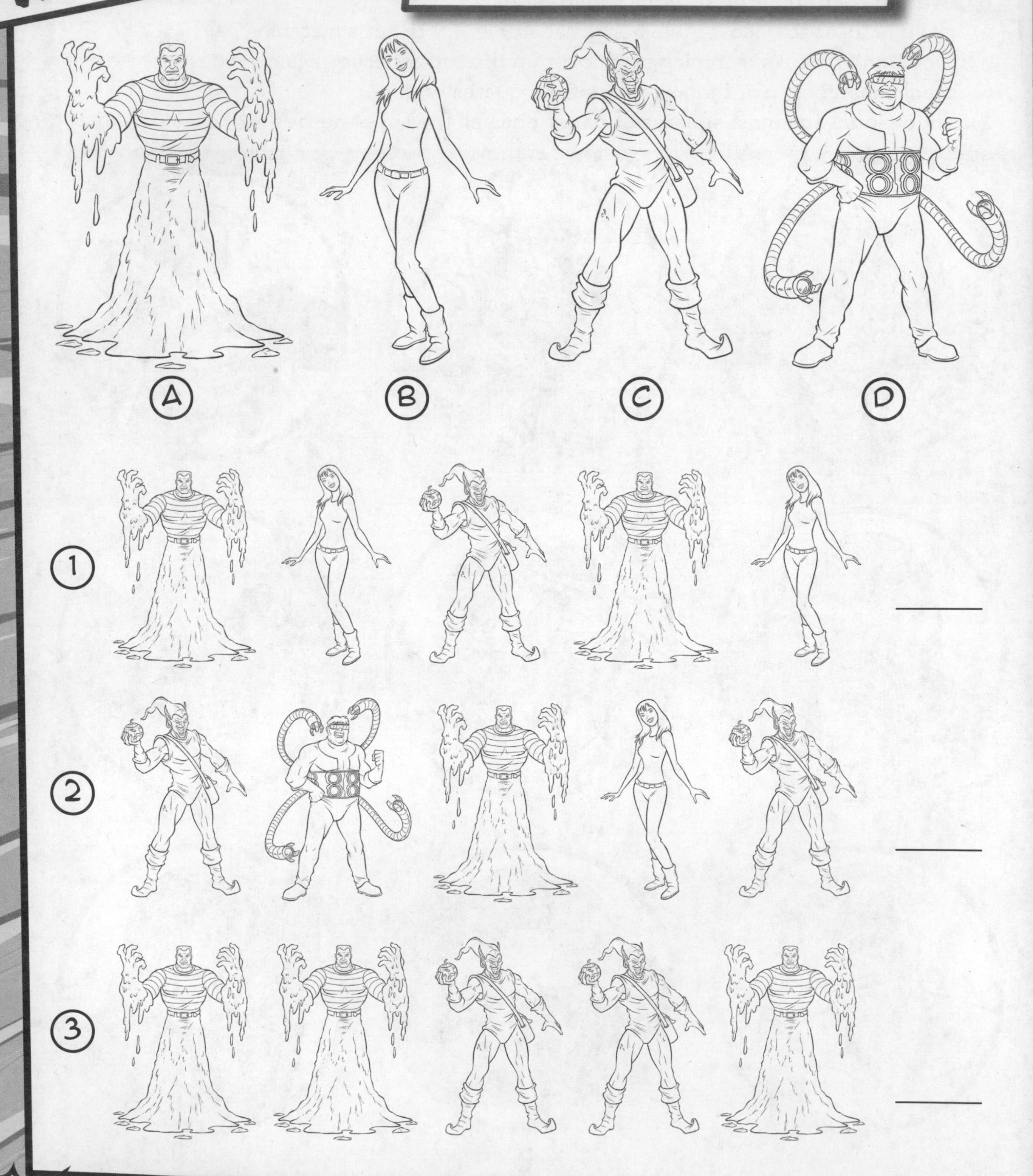

VILLAIN BLASTER!

Help Tony Stark design the ultimate super hero weapon. Remember, it must be powerful enough to take down the toughest villain!

ISLAND SEARCH

The Avengers are on a top-secret mission! Can you help them find their way to the Island of the Trolls?

START

FINISH

X-WORDS!
Put your word skills to the test! How many words can you make from the letters in the name PROFESSOR XAVIER? Play with a friend and see who can get the most words!

SUPER QUIZ

How good is your super hero knowledge? Answer these questions to find out how much you know about the Earth's mightiest heroes. Tick the correct answers.

1. WHO USES A HAMMER AS THEIR WEAPON?

A) IRON MAN
B) THOR
C) SPIDER-MAN

2. WHERE DOES SPIDER-MAN LIVE?

A) NEW YORK
B) PARIS
C) LONDON

3. WHICH ONE OF THESE IS NOT IN THE X-MEN?

A) CYCLOPS
B) STORM
C) HULK

4. IRON MAN'S SUIT IS RED AND WHICH OTHER COLOUR?

A) GREEN
B) GOLD
C) SILVER

5. THE HULK IS BRUCE WHO?

A) TANNER
B) BANNER
C) RANNER

LET'S SUIT UP!

Check out Iron Man's incredible armour!
Which Iron Man suit matches the one in the box?

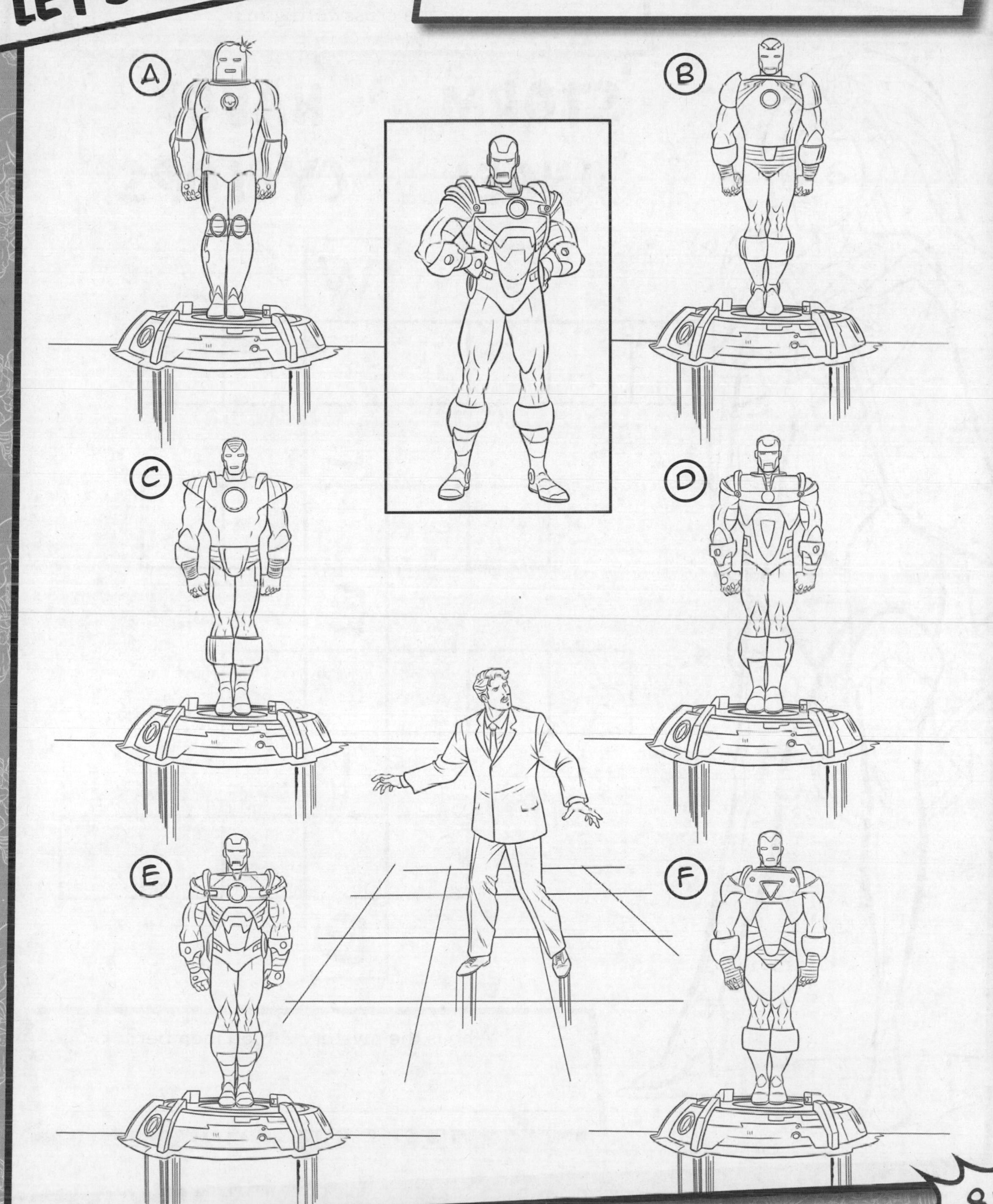

HIDDEN HERO

The X-Men have awesome mutant powers! Can you work out where each of these X-Men go in the crossword grid?

ALL CHANGE!

Spider-Man chases down Electro! Can you spot five differences in the picture on the right?

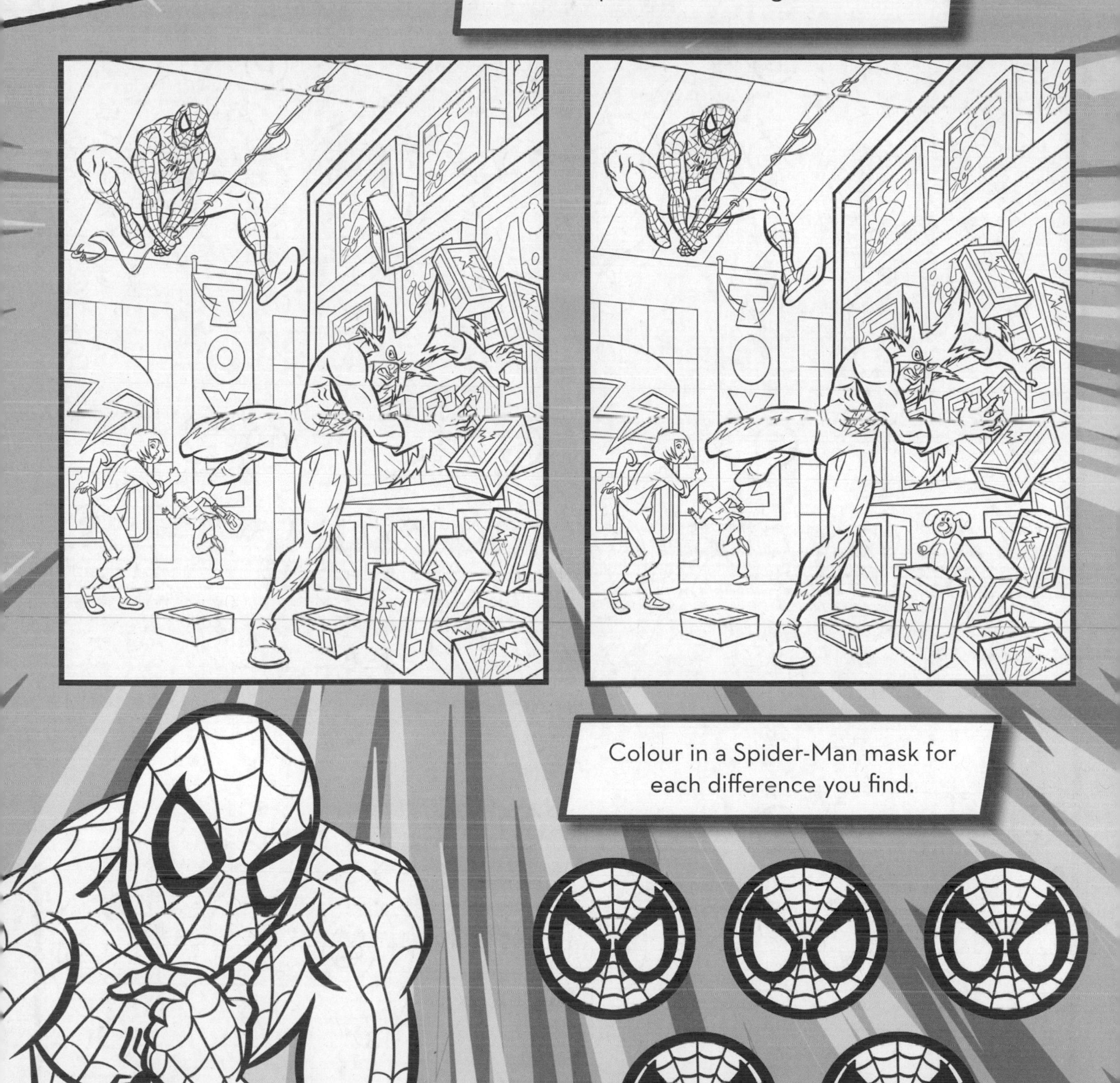

Colour in a Spider-Man mask for each difference you find.

ODD ONE OUT

Captain America is the world's greatest soldier! Which one is an imposter?

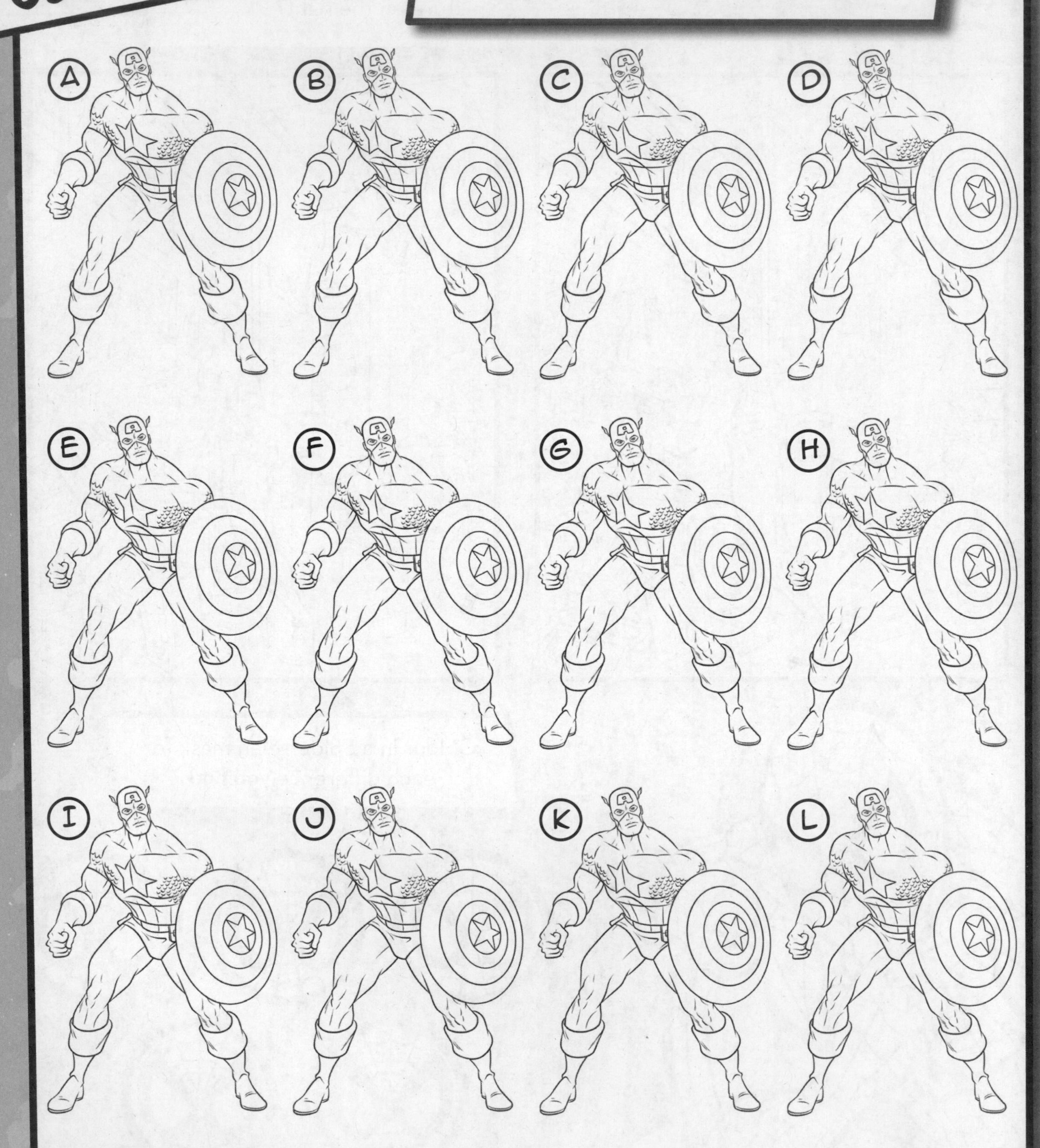

SUPER TRAIL

Which signal will take Iron Man to the Controller's hideout?

F

E

D

C

A

B

SHADOW MATCH

Hulk can smash through anything!
Which shadow matches Hulk exactly?

A

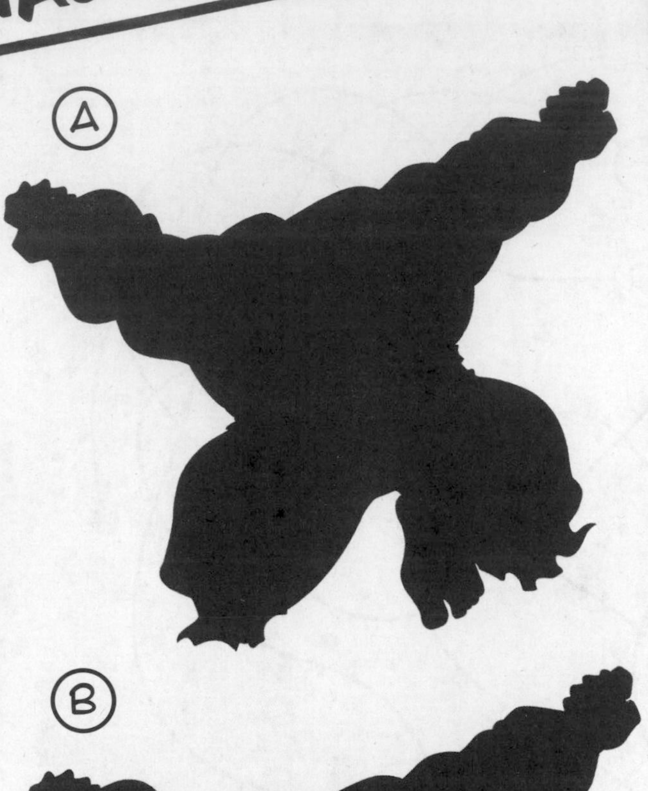

B

C

D

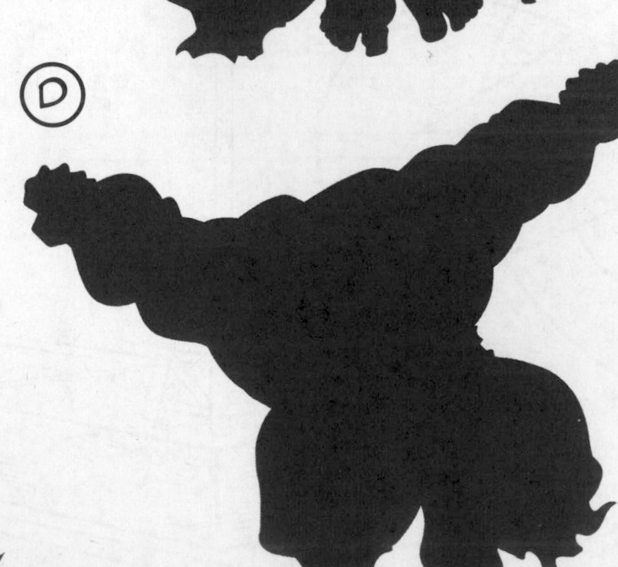

E

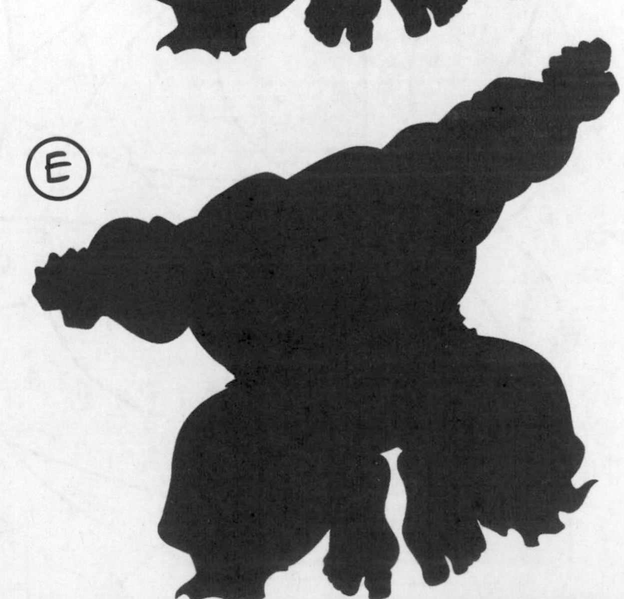

HERO SEARCH

Can you spot the 10 hero names in this wordsearch?

HULK WOLVERINE ANTMAN CYCLOPS IRON MAN
CAPTAIN AMERICA SPIDER-MAN THOR STORM WASP

W	K	W	O	L	V	E	R	I	N	E	G	W	E
A	L	A	N	T	M	A	N	R	W	S	I	A	P
T	U	B	A	K	W	P	F	O	A	T	C	S	R
J	H	R	O	I	T	B	E	N	M	O	E	P	H
C	A	P	T	A	I	N	A	M	E	R	I	C	A
S	H	U	N	I	A	T	W	A	T	M	N	I	E
S	P	I	D	E	R	M	A	N	I	D	L	M	V
R	C	Y	C	L	O	P	S	W	O	R	O	H	T

TOP HERO

Fight these villains by designing your own hero costume.

What would your hero name be?

STARK MESSAGE

Someone needs Iron Man's help! Can you help Tony Stark decode this message?

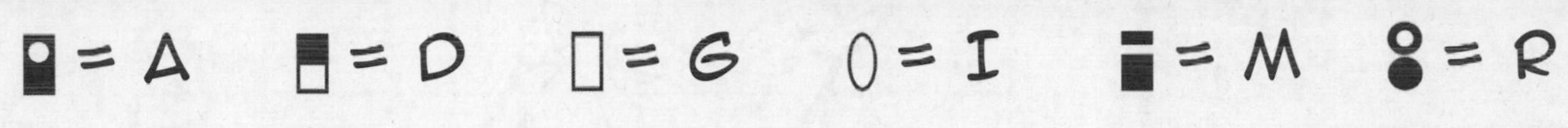

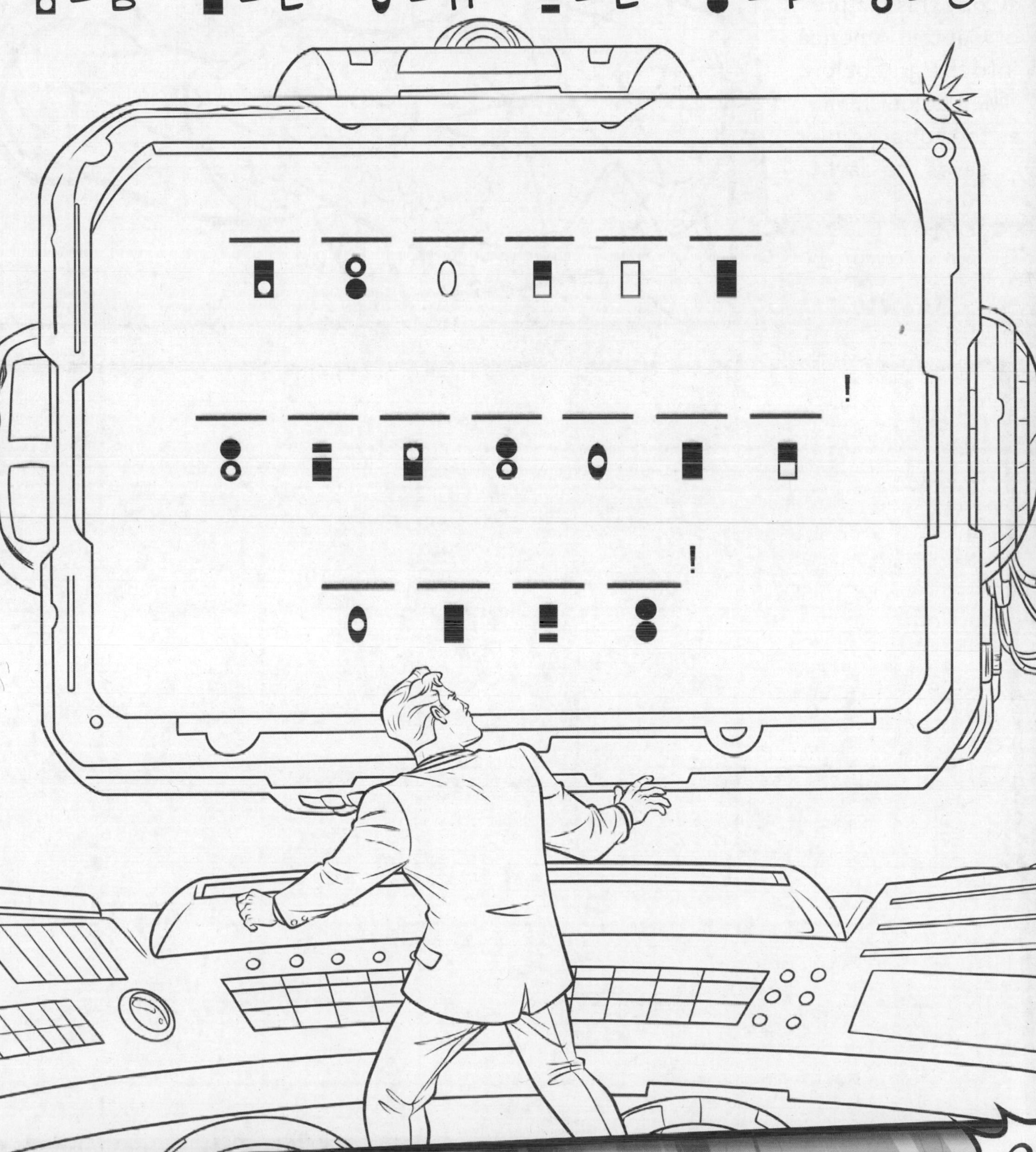

COPY CAP!

Copy this picture of Captain America into the grid below. Then colour him in as the super soldier saves the day!

ANSWERS

PAGE 38

1)  2)  3)  4)  5) 

PAGE 39

1) Thor, 2) Wolverine, 3) Iron Man, 4) Hulk, 5) Captain America

PAGES 40–41

It was a cold night in the city and trouble was in the air. **Spider-Man** had already been hard at work. A **bridge** had collapsed and he had to use **webs** to rebuild the **track** before the speeding **train** plummeted over the edge. As soon as the train was saved, the Green **Goblin** suddenly appeared.

"It's the end of the **line** for you!" shouted **Spider-Man**. Spider-Man **chased** the Green Goblin all across **New York**. As they fought, **people** watched in horror. Eventually, Spider-Man **chased** the Green Goblin so far away that the entire city of New York **cheered**. "**Hooray** for Spider-Man!" they shouted, as the city was saved once more.

PAGE 42

H

PAGE 44

1) Captain America, 2) Hulk

PAGE 46

D

PAGE 47

PAGE 48

1) Cyclops, 2) Beast, 3) Angel, 4) Wolverine, 5) Colossus

PAGE 50

F

PAGE 51

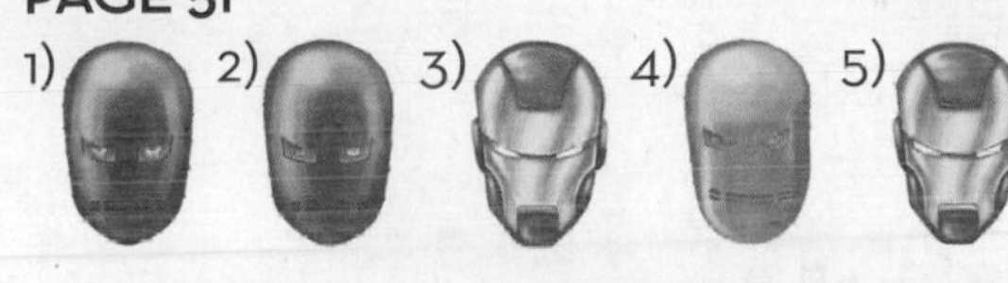

1) 2) 3) 4) 5)

PAGE 54

1) Spider-Man, 2) Storm, 3) Ice Man

PAGE 55

A) Captain America, B) Spider-Man, C) Thor, D) Hulk, E) Iron Man, F) Wolverine

PAGE 57

1) Iron Man, 2) Hulk, 3) Colossus, 4) Wolverine, 5) Thor

PAGE 58

1) Spider-Man, 2) Hulk, 3) Captain America, 4) Iron Man, 5) Colossus, 6) Ice Man

PAGE 59

A and E

PAGE 60

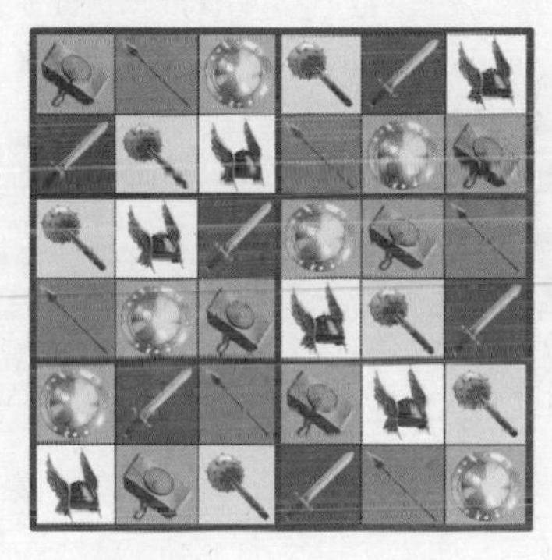

PAGE 61

C

PAGE 67

G

PAGE 69

1) B, 2) C, 3) A, 4) E, 5) D

PAGE 70

PAGE 71

```
MASK
  P
SHIELD
  D
GREEN
  R
HAMMER
  A
MEN
```

PAGE 72

W	A	S	P
S	P	A	W
A	W	P	S
P	S	W	A

H	U	L	K
L	K	U	H
U	H	K	L
K	L	H	U

PAGE 73
5 hammers and 7 swords

PAGE 74
D

PAGE 75
1) C, 2) A, 3) E, 4) F, 5) B, 6) D

PAGE 76
C

PAGE 77
Wolverine

PAGE 80
1) C, 2) D, 3) A

PAGE 82

PAGE 83
Possible answers: ape, ear, fox, pie, fire, pear, safe, fever, press, spies

PAGE 84
1) B, 2) A, 3) C, 4) B, 5) B

PAGE 85
E

PAGE 86

PAGE 87

PAGE 88
J

PAGE 89
A

PAGE 90
B

PAGE 91

```
W K W O L V E R I N E G W E
A L A N T M A N R W S I A P
T U B A K W P F O A T C S R
J H R O I T B E N M O E P H
C A P T A I N A M E R I C A
S H U N I A T W A T M N I E
S P I D E R M A N I D L M V
R C Y C L O P S W O R O H T
```

PAGE 93
Bridge smashed! Help!